GET OFF YOUR
F●●KING PHONE
FACTS AND ACTIVITIES FOR
SCREEN JUNKIES TO GET A LIFE

igloobooks

igloobooks

Published in 2020
by Igloo Books Ltd
Cottage Farm
Sywell
NN6 0BJ
www.igloobooks.com

Copyright © 2020 Igloo Books Ltd
Igloo Books is an imprint of Bonnier Books UK

0920 001
2 4 6 8 10 9 7 5 3 1
ISBN 978-1-83903-423-7

Cover, title pages, p58, 70, 107 and 176 imagery: © iStock / Getty Images
All other interior images courtesy of Shutterstock

Designed by Simon Parker
Edited by Claire Ormsby-Potter

Printed and manufactured in China

If it's the **Psychic Network** why do they need a **phone number?**

Robin Williams

NEED A REASON TO GET OFF YOUR PHONE?

Your phone may be carrying 10 times more bacteria than the average toilet seat. Studies show that some phones have more than 17,000 microbes, including *Streptococcus* and *E. coli.*

QUIZ:
ARE YOU ADDICTED TO YOUR PHONE?

1. When you're on your phone, how many times do friends and family need to ask you a question before you answer?

a) three times, then I look confused and they ask a fourth time

b) only once, I think. But they normally shake me or throw things when they ask questions, while seeming strangely annoyed

c) they just text me when they need to know anything

2. When you get to work, you realise you've left your phone at home, so you:

a) go straight home to get it, even though you'll miss that last-chance appraisal with your boss

b) that catastrophe could never happen as you're constantly on your phone as you travel, even though you ride a motorcycle to work

c) your phone has been surgically attached to your hand, so the whole question is so 20th century

3. When you shower, you put your phone:

   a) on the toilet seat, so you can hear if it pings

   b) in a plastic bag, so you can take it in with you

   c) you don't shower

4. Do you ever lose track of time when you're on your phone?

   a) yes, you forget to eat meals sometimes, but that's OK because you'll look slimmer in your Instagram posts

   b) yes, you once forgot to go to your great-aunt's funeral, but she wouldn't have wanted you to stop playing Candy Crush just when you'd got some boosters

   c) you've forgotten the last time you looked up from your phone, but maybe it was back when Twitter still had a 140-character limit

5. You usually text your friends to tell them:

   a) you'll text them to tell them you'll be texting to tell them you're heading to their house

   b) you're on the toilet

   c) you'd like them to shift over a bit as they're hampering your scrolling hand

Turn over for the answers.

ANSWERS:

Mostly **As**: Get off your phone.

Mostly **Bs**: Get off your *!*!ing phone.

Mostly **Cs**: **GET OFF YOUR *!*!ING PHONE! YOU £*$&!%!!**

ALTERNATIVE THINGS TO DO WITH YOUR PHONE #1

USE IT AS A DOORSTOP.

WHY DOES ANYONE HAVE A LANDLINE?

TO FIND THEIR MOBILE WHEN IT GOES MISSING.

WHERE'S WILL?
CAN YOU FIND HIM?

Turn over for the answer.

The first tweet was sent by Jack Dorsey, CEO of Twitter, in 2006.

It read: *'just setting up my twttr'*.

QUIZ:
DO YOU KNOW EVERYTHING THERE IS TO KNOW ABOUT PHONES?

• •

1. In which year did Martin Cooper of Motorola make the first mobile phone call to Dr Joel Engel of Bell Labs?

a) 1973

b) 1983

c) 1993

2. Which country has the most mobile phone users?

a) The United States

b) Russia

c) China

3. In which year did IBM sell the first smartphone?

a) 1992

b) 1993

c) 1994

• •

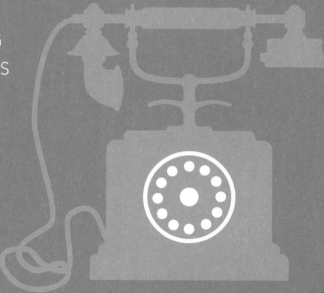

4. Who is <u>not</u> credited with inventing the telephone?
   a) Alexander Graham Bell
   b) Michael Faraday
   c) Antonio Meucci

5. Which iPhone launched in 2007?
   a) iPhone 3G
   b) iPhone 2G
   c) iPnone 3GS

'Never trust
anything
you read on
the Internet.'

Abraham Lincoln

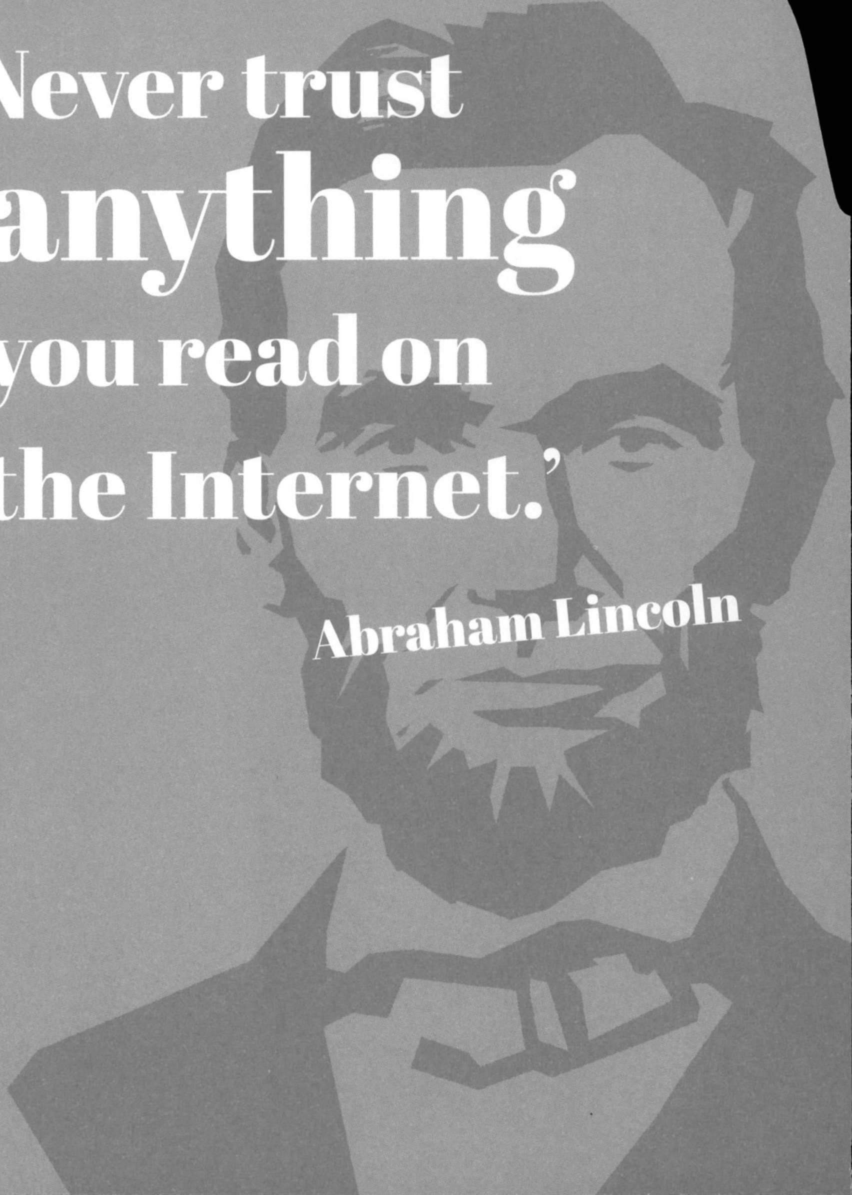

HAVE YOU EVER PUT YOUR PHONE DOWN AND TRIED DOING THINGS WITH TWO HANDS, LIKE IN THE GOOD OLD DAYS?

. . . .

ALTERNATIVE THINGS TO DO WITH YOUR PHONE #2

MAKE YOUR DOG HAPPY BY PLAYING FETCH WITH IT.

YOUR MOBILE PHONE HAS MORE COMPUTING POWER THAN THE COMPUTERS USED ON *APOLLO 11*, WHICH CARRIED THE FIRST MEN TO THE MOON.

So why are you using it to send poo emojis?

SPOT THE DIFFERENCE
CAN YOU SPOT FIVE DIFFERENCES?

Turn over for the answer.

Did you spot them?

HOW DID PEOPLE LET EVERYONE KNOW THEY'D BOUGHT A NEW CAR BEFORE THEY INVENTED PHONES?

A MAN IS DRIVING HOME
FROM WORK WHEN HE GETS
A CALL FROM HIS WIFE.

'JOHN!' SHE CRIES,
'BE CAREFUL OUT THERE.
I HEARD SOME FOOL IS
SO BUSY TALKING ON HIS
PHONE THAT HE'S DRIVING
THE WRONG WAY DOWN
THE MOTORWAY!'

'IT'S NOT JUST ONE IDIOT,'
HE REPLIES, 'THERE ARE
HUNDREDS OF THEM.'

EVERY YEAR, MORE PEOPLE DIE WHILE TAKING SELFIES THAN FROM SHARK ATTACKS. ON AVERAGE, AROUND 40 PEOPLE DIE TAKING SELFIES, WHILE FEWER THAN 10 DIE IN THE JAWS OF A SHARK.

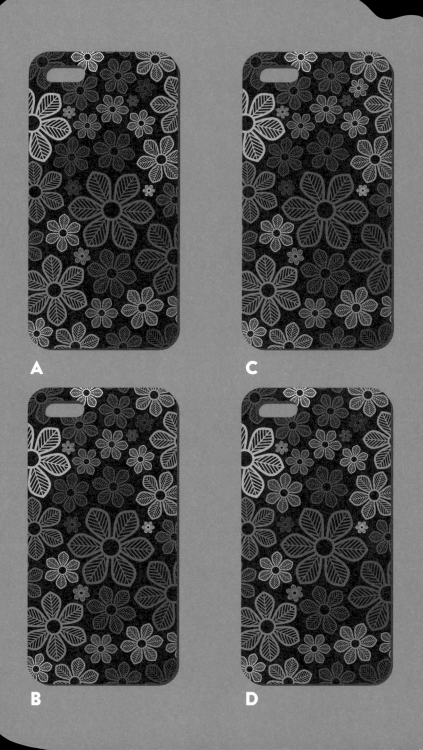

A

C

B

D

E

G

F

. . . .

FIND THE PAIR
WHICH TWO PHONE CASES ARE IDENTICAL?

. . . .

ANSWER: B and G

ALTERNATIVE THINGS TO DO WITH YOUR PHONE #3

USE IT TO PROP UP A WOBBLY TABLE LEG.

LEFT MY PHONE UNDER MY PILLOW LAST NIGHT AND WHEN I WOKE UP IT WAS GONE AND THERE WAS MONEY THERE.

I THINK IT WAS THE BLUETOOTH FAIRY.

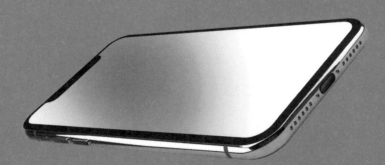

A WOMAN DROPPED HER PHONE FROM THE 18TH FLOOR OF AN OFFICE BLOCK.

GOOD THING IT WAS IN AEROPLANE MODE.

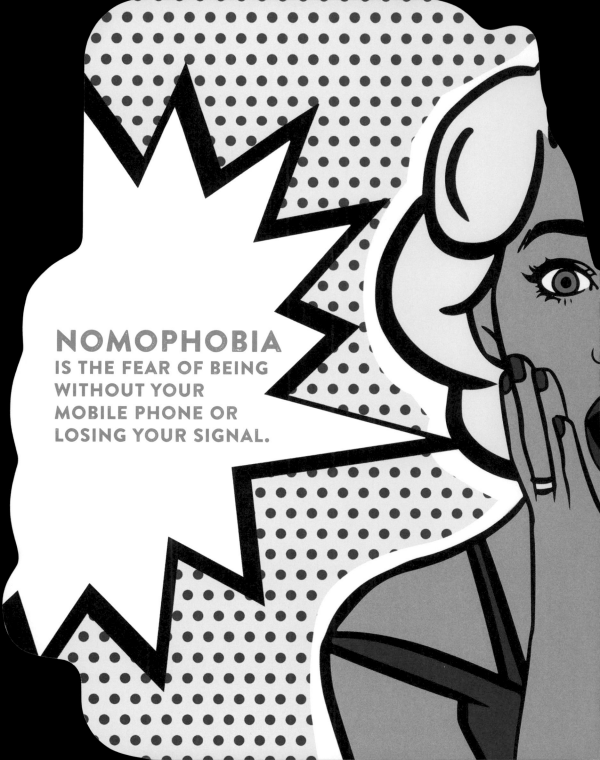

A WOMAN GOT A NEW MOBILE PHONE FOR HER HUSBAND.

SHE CONSIDERED IT A PRETTY GOOD TRADE-OFF.

ALTERNATIVE THINGS TO DO WITH YOUR PHONE #4

SKIM IT ACROSS A POND TO SEE HOW MANY TIMES IT WILL BOUNCE.

. . . .

IF ONLY YOU COULD
PULL YOUR SELFIE
FACE THE WHOLE
TIME... AND GET
EVERYONE TO STAND
JUST ABOVE YOU
AND TO THE LEFT.

. . . .

HELP PHILIPPA FIND HER PHONE

Turn over for the answer.

ANSWER

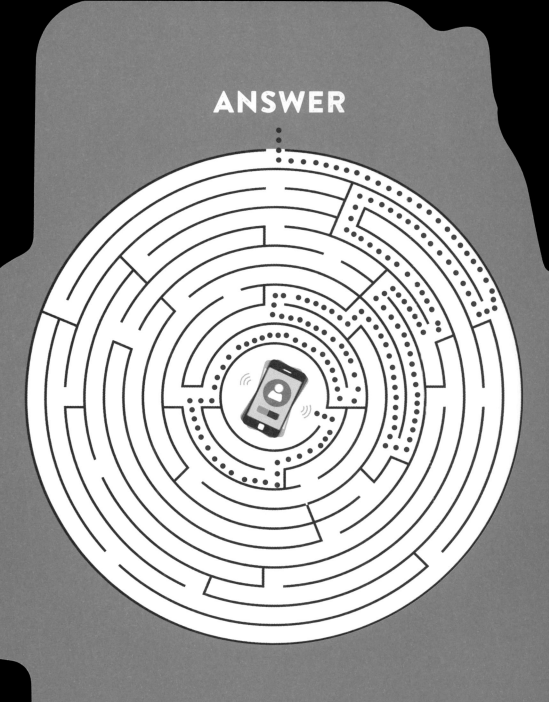

'Brevity is the soul
of wit. 'Tis a rare
challenge to rein
one's galloping wits
into 140 characters.'

William Shakespeare

A

C

D

DATING APP GUESS WHO

Amelia would like to date someone who:

a) wears a hat

b) does not wear glasses

c) does wear earrings

Who should she pick?

E

F

G

H

TWO FRIENDS ARE SITTING
IN THE CINEMA WAITING
FOR THE FILM TO START.
THE STANDARD
ANNOUNCEMENT COMES ON,
REMINDING EVERYONE TO
TURN OFF THEIR PHONES.
ONE OF THE FRIENDS YELPS
WITH ANNOYANCE, JUMPS UP
AND GRABS HIS COAT.

'WHAT'S THE MATTER?' SAYS HIS FRIEND, 'CAN'T EVEN SIT THROUGH A FILM WITHOUT YOUR PHONE ON?'

'THAT'S NOT THE PROBLEM,' SAYS HIS FRIEND, 'I LEFT IT AT HOME.'

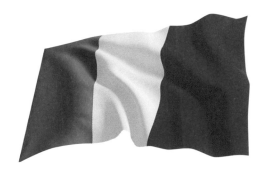

I GOT A TEXT SAYING THAT ITALY WOULD WIN THE WORLD CUP.

PREDICTIVE TEXTS DRIVE ME MAD.

. . . .

When Alexander Graham Bell invented the telephone, he already had three missed calls from accident claim companies.

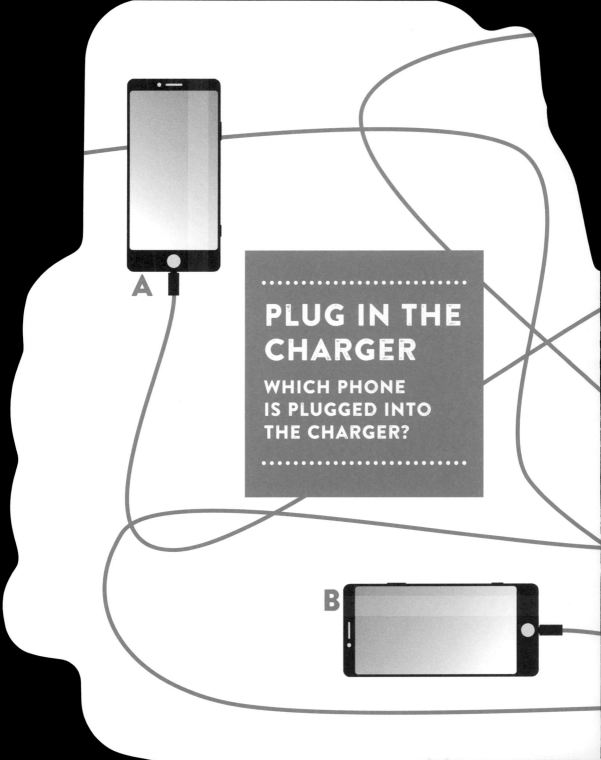

A

PLUG IN THE CHARGER

WHICH PHONE IS PLUGGED INTO THE CHARGER?

B

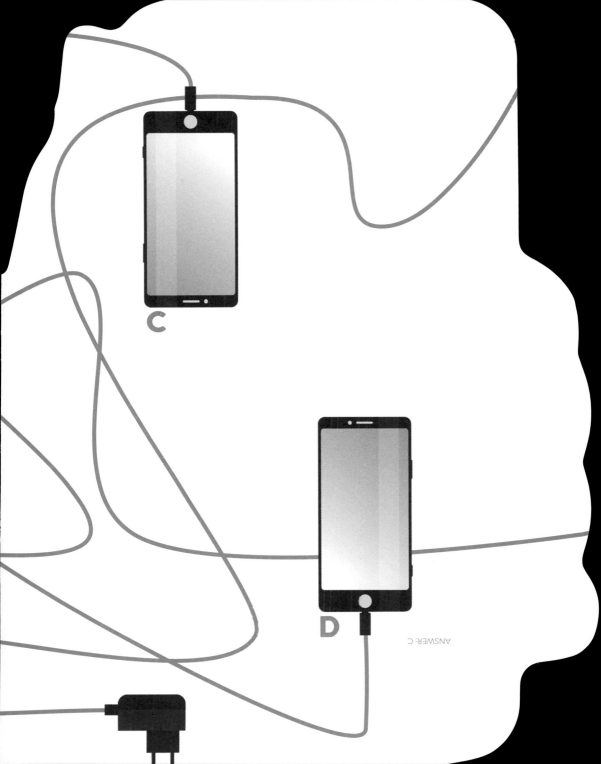

C

D

ANSWER: C

HOW DID PEOPLE EVER MANAGE TO FIND WHERE THEIR FRIENDS WERE WAITING FOR THEM BEFORE THEY INVENTED PHONES?

....

THE TECHNOLOGY
THAT RUNS
SMARTPHONES IS
BASED ON 250,000
INDIVIDUAL PATENTS.

SHAME YOU'RE NOT
SMART ENOUGH
TO FIND YOUR
SMARTPHONE WHEN
IT'S FALLEN BEHIND
THE SOFA CUSHION.

....

QUIZ:
DO YOU OVERSHARE ON SOCIAL MEDIA?

1. You post photos of the food on your plate when:

   a) you're in a fancy restaurant

   b) you're in McDonald's

   c) you open a packet of crackers

2. You feel you have to let everyone know when you:

   a) have a bowel movement

   b) haven't had a bowel movement in longer than 4 hours

   c) think maybe you might go to the bathroom, just to have a try

3. You post photos of yourself every time you:

   a) take a mini break

   b) take a trip to Tesco

   c) take out the bins

4. You use social media to vent your deeply held opinions about:

a) the climate crisis (it's important to let everyone know how you feel, because that's the starting point for global change)

b) the neighbour's shrub that's overgrowing your property (it's important to let everyone know how you feel, because this affects us all)

c) the fact that someone's finished the last of the milk in the fridge (it's important to let everyone know how you feel, because your friends and family have really dull lives compared with yours, so they only live for your next post)

5. You always post when:

a) you get lucky

b) you're in the middle of getting lucky

c) it's safest just to live stream on your YouTube channel

ANSWERS: Mostly **As:** Nobody cares.

Mostly **Bs:** Nobody cares, you narcissistic idiot.

Mostly **Cs:** Search for "self-centredness". Look, someone's linked to your Facebook page!

**DON'T YOU HATE
IT WHEN PEOPLE
ADD POINTLESS
EMOJIS TO
EVERY TEXT?** 💩

BEEP-BEEP-BEEP ... BEEP-BEE
BEEP-BEEP-BEEP-BEEP-BEEP...
BEEP-BEEP-BEEP-BEEP... BEE
... ... BEEP-... ... ...BEEP-BEEP ... B
EP-BEEP-BEEP-BEEP-BEEP-BEE
BEEP-BEEP... BEEP-BEEP BEEP BE
BEEP

WHY DO SOME PEOPLE HAVE VOLUME ON THEIR KEYPADS?

EP. BEEP-BEEP-BEEP-BEEP ... BEEP-BE
EP... BEEP-BEEP-BEEP-BEEP BEEP-BEE
EP-BEEP-BEEP-BEEP... BEEP-BEEP-BEE
EP... BEEP.BEEP-BEEP-BEEP-BEEP ... B
EP ... BEEP-BEEP BEEP-BEEP-BEEP-BE
EP-BEEP-BEEP-BEEP... BEEP-BEEP-BEE
EP... BEEP. BEEP-BEEP-BEEP-BEEP ... B
EP-BEEP-BEEP-BEEP... BEEP BEEP BEE
EP-BEEP-BEEP-BEEP... BEEP BEEPEEP
P-BEEP... BEEP BEEPEEP-BEEP BEEP-
BEEP BEEPEEP-BEEP BEEP-BEEP-

BEEP-
EP-BEEP-
BEEP...
EP-BEEP
EP... BEEP-
BEEP BEEP
EEP BEEP
BEEP BEE
EEP BEEP
EP-BEEP
-BEEP-BE
P-BEEP... BE
EP-BEEP-
P-BEEP-BEEP...
P-BEEP... BEEP-
EEP-BEEP-BEEP
EEP-BEEP
EEP BEEP-
EEP-BEEP-
EEP-BEEP...

ALTERNATIVE THINGS TO DO WITH YOUR PHONE #5

SEARCH FOR ALIEN LIFE. SETI USES MOBILE PHONES TO ANALYSE RADIO TELESCOPE DATA. IT'S FREE TO PARTICIPATE THROUGH THE SETI WEBSITE.

WHAT IS THE CHEAPEST TIME TO CALL YOUR FRIENDS LONG DISTANCE?

WHEN THEIR PHONE IS OFF.

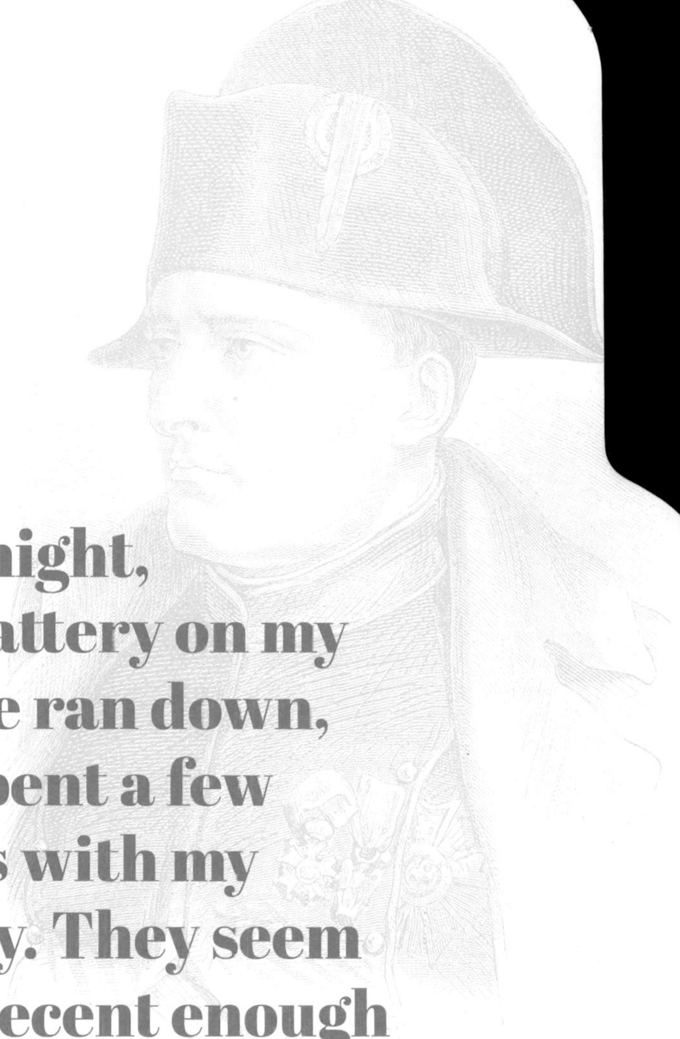

'Last night,
the battery on my
phone ran down,
so I spent a few
hours with my
family. They seem
like decent enough
people.'

Napoleon Bonaparte

SCIENTISTS HAVE DEVELOPED
A MOBILE PHONE CHARGER THAT
MAKES ENERGY USING URINE.
THE MICROBIAL FUEL CELL CAN
PROVIDE 3 HOURS OF PHONE
CALLS FROM 600 ML OF URINE.

UNFORTUNATELY, YOU DON'T GET
FREE CALLS JUST FROM DROPPING
YOUR PHONE IN THE TOILET.

SPOT THE DIFFERENCE
CAN YOU SPOT FIVE DIFFERENCES?

Turn over for the answer.

Did you spot them?

'I declare I shall not call it a "smartphone" until it can speak up to inform me which couch cushion it is hiding behind.'

Sir Isaac Newton

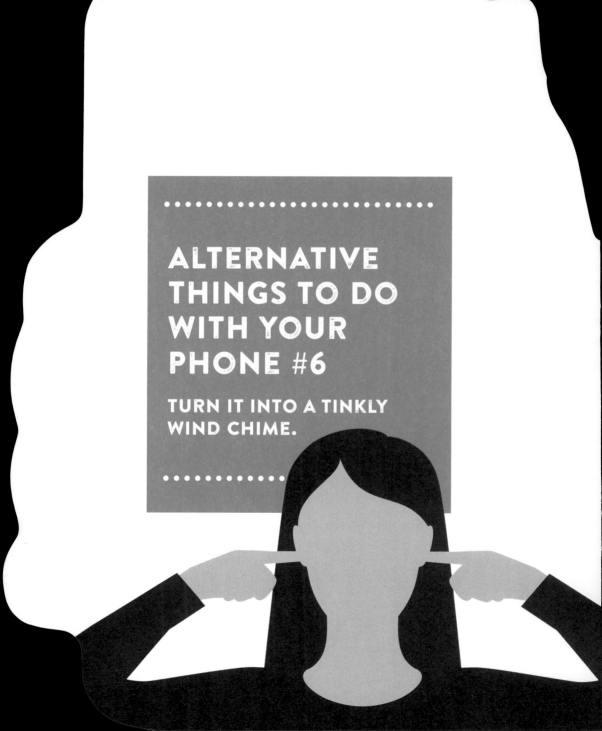

ALTERNATIVE
THINGS TO DO
WITH YOUR
PHONE #6

TURN IT INTO A TINKLY
WIND CHIME.

PHONE EVOLUTION

WHICH TWO ROWS OF PHONES ARE IDENTICAL?

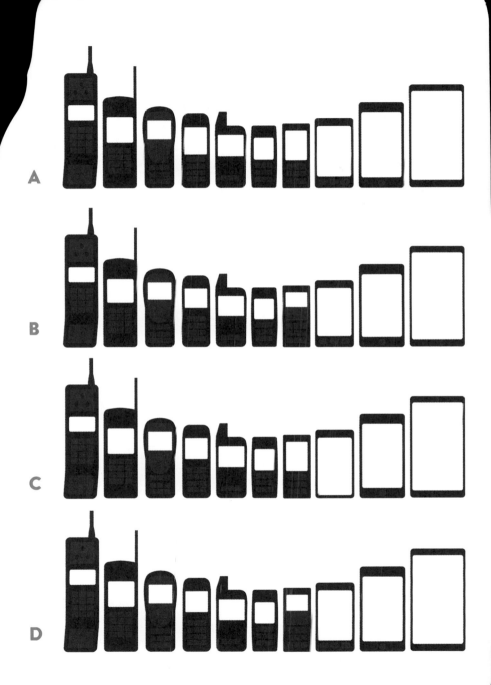

ALTERNATIVE THINGS TO DO WITH YOUR PHONE #7

GO TO THE BEACH AND USE IT AS A SPADE.

DAVID CONTORNO OF ILLINOIS, IN THE UNITED STATES, HAS HAD THE SAME MOBILE NUMBER SINCE 1985, WHEN HE BOUGHT AN AMERITECH AC140.

JUST THINK OF ALL THE COLD-CALLING LISTS HE MUST BE ON!

'How is it that, if our friends fall, we laugh; but if our phone falls, we panic?'

Oscar Wilde

NEVER EVER TURN
YOUR PHONE
TO SILENT.

HOW WILL YOU EVER
FIND IT AGAIN?

WHERE'S WILL?
CAN YOU FIND HIM?

Turn over for the answer.

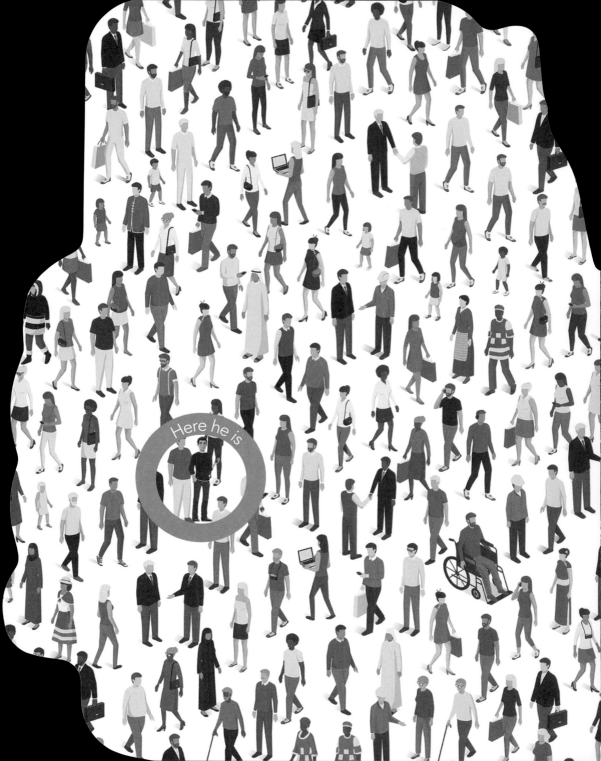

DID YOU MISS
YOUR CHILD
TAKING HER FIRST
STEPS... BECAUSE
YOU WERE TRYING
TO FIND YOUR
PHONE TO VIDEO
HER TAKING HER
FIRST STEPS?

Night after night, Susan looks out of her window and sees a handsome young man standing on the pavement. He never tries to speak to her, but he steals swift glances at her through the window, then looks shyly at his mobile. Susan realises he is in love with her, but cannot pick up the courage to tell her how he feels. He looks so lovelorn that she starts to have feelings for him in return. After several months, she decides to go outside and tell the handsome young man that she has fallen in love with him, too.

When the young man has heard her expression of love, he looks deeply shaken.

'I'm sorry,' he gasps, 'It's just that you've got no password on your wi-fi, so I come here to chat with my girlfriend.'

ALTERNATIVE THINGS TO DO WITH YOUR PHONE #8

HAVE FUN WITH YOUR FRIENDS BY USING IT AS A FRISBEE.

A

B

C

D

E

F

G

H

DATING APP GUESS WHO

Jill would like to date someone who:

a) does not wear purple

b) has a moustache

c) wears glasses

Who should she pick?

I J

K L

M N

O P

THE LARGEST
FUNCTIONING MOBILE
PHONE WAS MADE BY
SAMSUNG IN 2009.
IT MEASURED
4.57 X 3.42 X 0.74 M.

AT LEAST YOU'D NEVER
ACCIDENTALLY LEAVE IT
ON THE PASSENGER SEAT.

HOW DID PEOPLE FEEL INSECURE OVER WHAT EVERYONE ELSE WAS ACHIEVING BEFORE THEY INVENTED PHONES?

QUIZ:
DO YOU PLAY TOO MANY GAMES?
(AND WHAT GAMES ARE YOU PLAYING?)

1. When at the supermarket, do you feel an overwhelming urge to group the candies into threes by colour? Y/N

2. Do you spot large-eyed, brightly coloured monsters every time you take a walk? Y/N

3. If you visit a train station, do you grab your skateboard then leap onto the roof of a train? Y/N

4. Are you always looking over your shoulder for creepers? Y/N

5. Do you run everywhere you go, swiping with your thumb when you need to change direction? Y/N

6. When getting yourself a glass of water, do you pour from a great height, with the glass dangling at a peculiar angle? Y/N

7. Are you picky about who can join your clan? Y/N

8. When making a fruit salad, do you ask someone to throw the fruit in the air so you can slice it with a machete? Y/N

9. Do you keep your pickaxe with you at all times? Y/N

10. Every time you see a pig, do you try to stuff a bird into a slingshot? Y/N

FACT:
9 OUT OF 10 TEXT
MESSAGES ARE READ
WITHIN 3 MINUTES
OF DELIVERY.

UNLESS IT'S THE TEXT
ASKING YOU TO PICK UP
SOME MILK ON THE WAY
HOME FROM WORK.

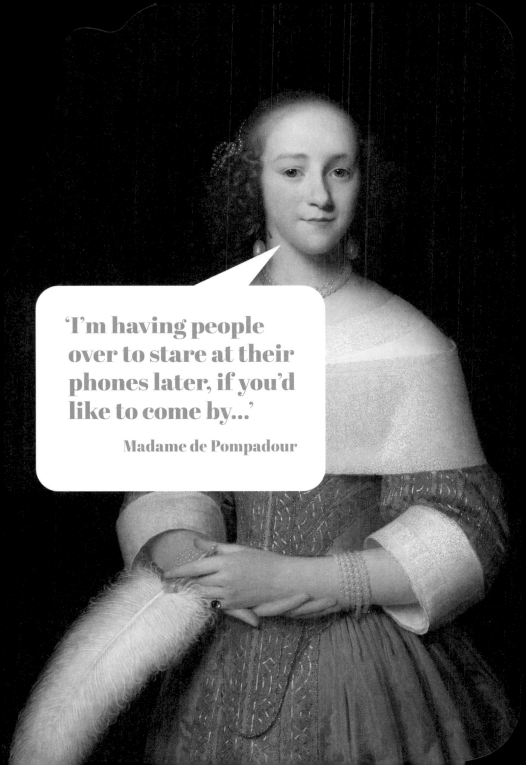

ALTERNATIVE THINGS TO DO WITH YOUR PHONE #9

USE IT TO SCRAPE ICE OFF YOUR CAR WINDSCREEN.

THE SPORT OF MOBILE PHONE-THROWING BEGAN IN FINLAND IN 2000. THE BEST THROW OF ALL TIME WAS BY DRIES FEREMANS OF BELGIUM, IN 2014: 110.4 M.

COULD YOU BEAR TO STOP CHECKING YOUR FEED FOR LONG ENOUGH TO HAVE A GO?

FORENSIC SCIENTISTS CAN TELL
WHAT HAIRCARE PRODUCTS
YOU USE, FOOD YOU EAT AND
MEDICINES YOU TAKE FROM THE
RESIDUE THEY LEAVE ON YOUR
MOBILE. SOME CHEMICALS, SUCH
AS THE MOSQUITO REPELLENT
DEET, STAY ON A PHONE FOR
4 MONTHS AFTER THE PRODUCT
WAS LAST USED.

SO, IF YOU COMMIT A CRIME
AGAINST A MOSQUITO, MAKE
SURE YOU STAY OFF YOUR PHONE.

SPOT THE DIFFERENCE
CAN YOU SPOT FIVE DIFFERENCES?

TURN OVER FOR THE ANSWER.

DID YOU SPOT THEM?

THE FASTEST
KNOWN TEXTER IS
NORWEGIAN SONJA
KRISTIANSEN, WHO
TOOK 37.28 SECONDS
TO TYPE THIS
MESSAGE:

'The razor-toothed piranhas of the genera Serrasalmus and Pygocentrus are the most ferocious freshwater fish in the world. In reality, they seldom attack a human.'

BUT SHE
FORGOT TO SIGN
OFF WITH A 'LOL'
SO IT DOESN'T
REALLY COUNT.

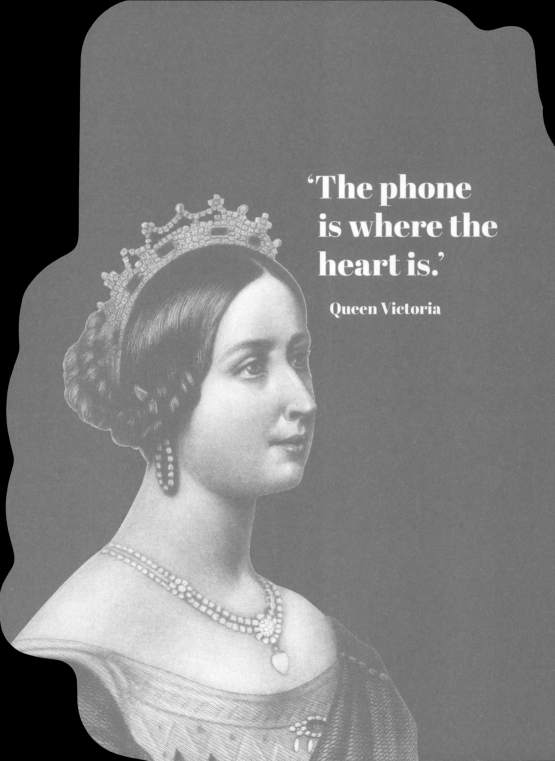

'The phone
is where the
heart is.'

Queen Victoria

One lunchtime, the mobile phone on Steve's desk rings. He picks it up and turns it to speaker.

'Hi, darling,' says a woman's voice, 'I'm in the Porsche showroom. Do you mind if I upgrade to the £90,000 model?'

'No, sweetie,' replies Steve. 'If that's what you want, just go for it.'

Everyone in the office gathers around Steve, open-mouthed.

'On the way home,' says the woman's voice, 'I thought I'd stop by the jeweller's and pick up that ring I fancied. They're having a sale, so it's down to £16,000.'

'Absolutely,' says Steve. 'Money is no object.'

'In that case,' says the woman, 'I'll pick up the emerald bracelet as well.'

'Great!' replies Steve. 'Love you!'

'Love you too!'

Steve ends the call, then turns to look at his astonished colleagues. 'Anyone know whose phone this is?'

ALTERNATIVE THINGS TO DO WITH YOUR PHONE #10

GIVE IT TO SOME PRESCHOOLERS SO THEY CAN PLAY PRETEND.

DON'T SHARE YOUR EAR BUDS: THEY CAN TRANSFER WAX, BACTERIA, FUNGUS AND EAR MITES FROM PERSON TO PERSON.

If you don't know what ear mites are,
Google them – or just examine your ear buds.

HELP FIONN FIND HIS PHONE

TURN OVER FOR THE ANSWER.

DID HE FIND IT?

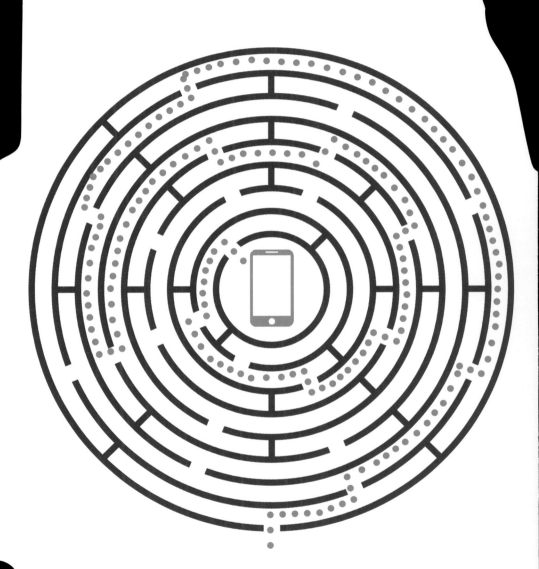

THE FIRST HAND-HELD, PORTABLE MOBILE PHONES WENT ON SALE IN THE UNITED STATES IN 1984, COSTING A WHOPPING $3,995.

Still less expensive than roaming charges, though.

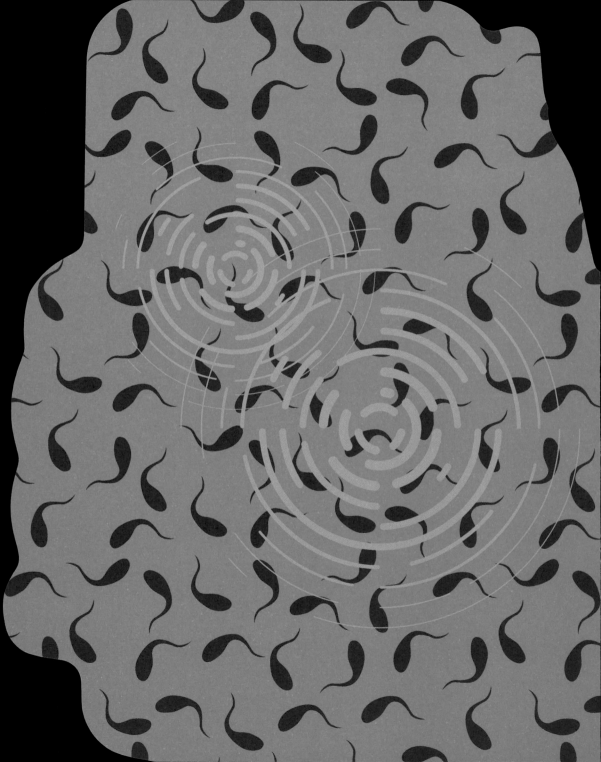

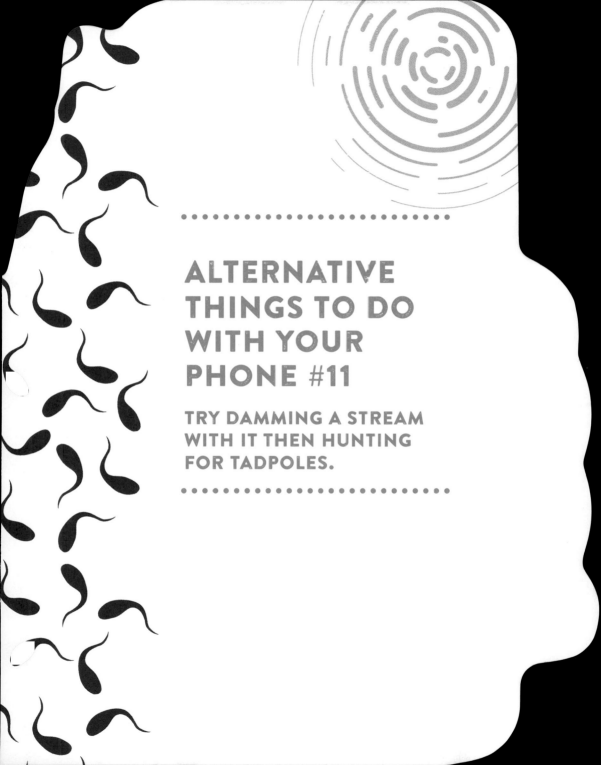

ALTERNATIVE THINGS TO DO WITH YOUR PHONE #11

TRY DAMMING A STREAM WITH IT THEN HUNTING FOR TADPOLES.

THE FIRST THREE
PEOPLE TO SIGN UP
TO FACEBOOK IN 2004
WERE COFOUNDERS
MARK ZUCKERBERG
(ID 4), CHRIS HUGHES
(ID 5) AND DUSTIN
MOSKOVITZ (ID 6).
IDS 1–3 WERE PROBABLY
CREATED AS TESTS BUT
NO LONGER EXIST.

BUT WHAT WERE THEIR
RELATIONSHIP STATUSES?

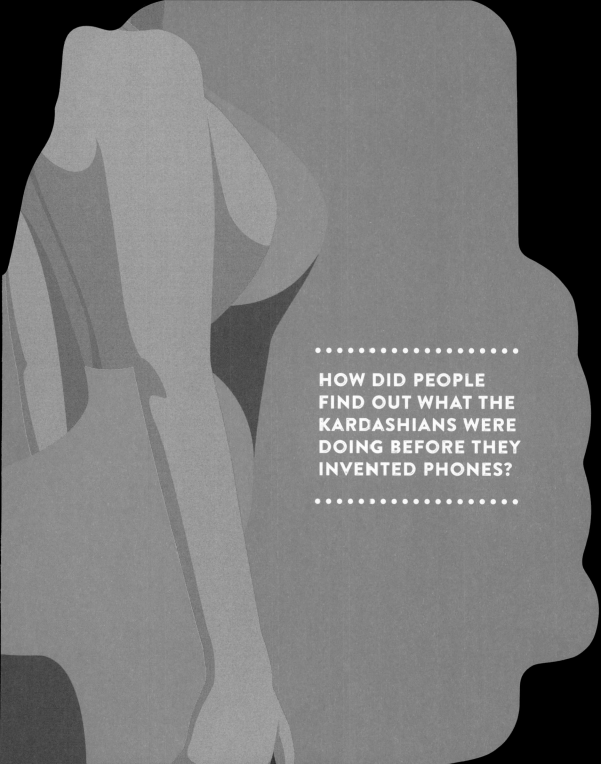

HOW DID PEOPLE
FIND OUT WHAT THE
KARDASHIANS WERE
DOING BEFORE THEY
INVENTED PHONES?

June calls her husband's phone to find out why he's taking so long to walk the dog.

'Aaah, my love,' he replies. **'Do you remember that little jewellers with those diamond earrings that you fell in love with when we were first married? I couldn't afford to buy them for you then, but I promised that, if I ever had the money, I would get you the gift you deserved?'**

'I do remember!' she gasps.

'Well, I'm in the strip club next to that.'

HAVE YOU EVER TEXTED
A FRIEND WHEN HE WAS
SITTING RIGHT NEXT
TO YOU?

SAVES HAVING TO SPEAK
IN FULL SENTENCES,
DOESN'T IT?

FIND THE PAIR
Which two phone cases are identical?

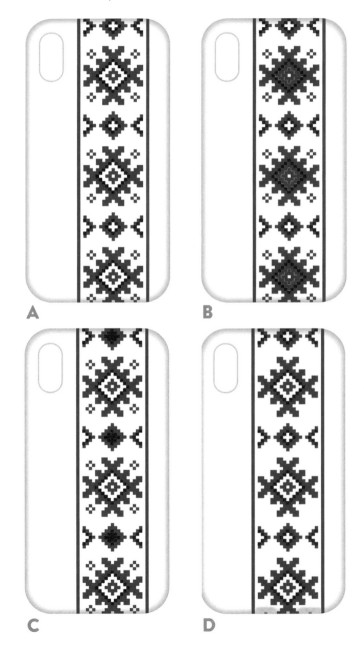

A

B

C

D

E

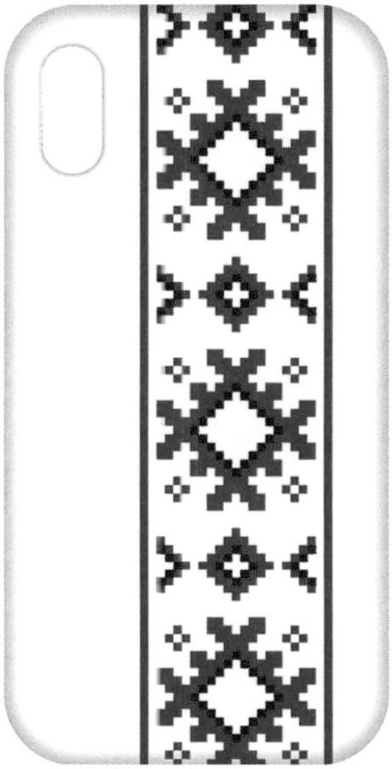

F

G

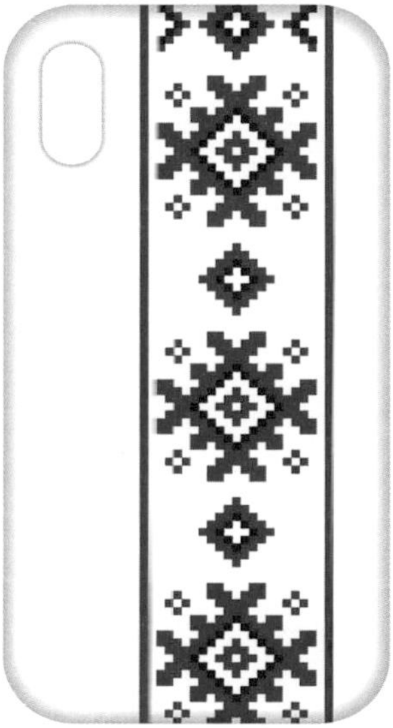

H

HOW DID PEOPLE KNOW
WHAT THEIR MOTHER'S
NEIGHBOUR'S FRIEND'S
DAUGHTER'S NEW DECKING
LOOKED LIKE BEFORE THEY
INVENTED PHONES?

'How is it that when my phone is on silent, I have 10 missed calls? Yet when I turn the volume to maximum, nobody calls?'

Leonardo da Vinci

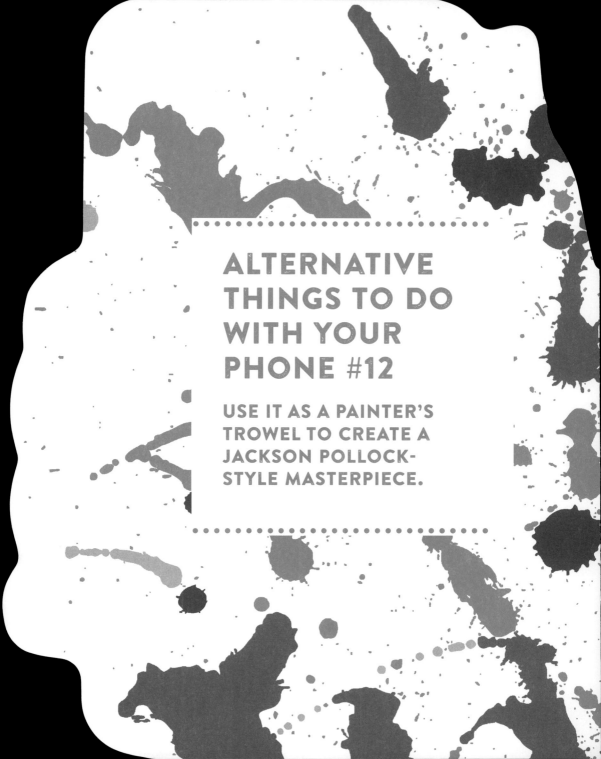

ALTERNATIVE THINGS TO DO WITH YOUR PHONE #12

USE IT AS A PAINTER'S TROWEL TO CREATE A JACKSON POLLOCK-STYLE MASTERPIECE.

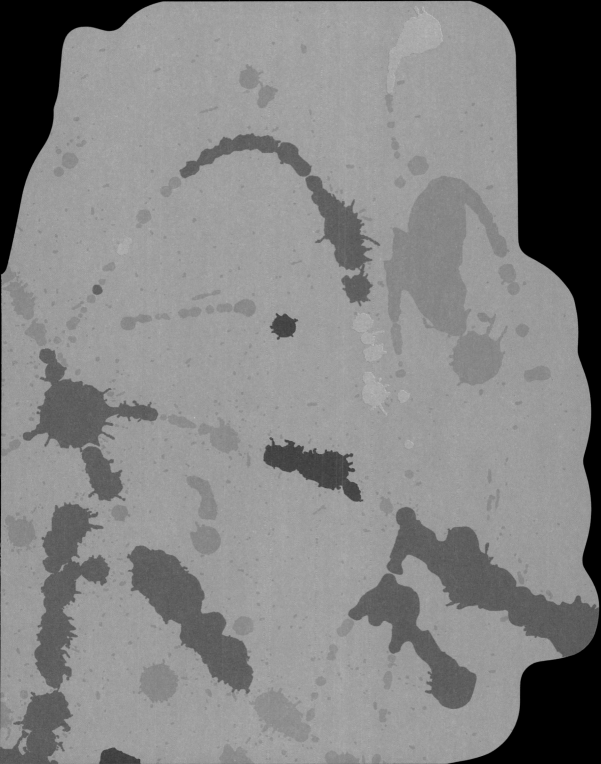

QUIZ:
DO YOU KNOW YOUR APPS?

....

1. How many apps are downloaded globally every year?

   a) More than 100 billion

   b) More than 200 billion

   c) More than 300 billion

2. In which year was the ground-breaking Snake app preloaded for the first time on the brand-new Nokia 6110 phone?

   a) 1994

   b) 1996

   c) 1998

....

. . . .

3. What was the most downloaded game app of the 2010s?

    a) Subway Surfers

    b) Candy Crush Saga

    c) Temple Run 2

4. In which year did the App Store open?

    a) 2008

    b) 2003

    c) 1998

5. Which app merged with Musical.ly in 2017?

    a) Shazam

    b) TikTok

    c) Musixmatch

. . . .

· ·

MORE PEOPLE IN THE WORLD
HAVE ACCESS TO A MOBILE
THAN TO A FLUSHING TOILET.
AROUND 6 BILLION PEOPLE
CAN USE A MOBILE, BUT ONLY
4.5 BILLION CAN USE A SAFE
AND HYGIENIC TOILET.

· ·

SPOT THE DIFFERENCE
CAN YOU SPOT FIVE DIFFERENCES?

TURN OVER FOR THE ANSWER.

DID YOU SPOT THEM?

HOW CAN YOU TELL WHICH
OF YOUR FRIENDS HAS THE
LATEST PHONE MODEL?

DON'T WORRY, THEY'LL
MAKE SURE THEY TELL YOU.

ALTERNATIVE THINGS TO DO WITH YOUR PHONE #13

USE IT TO HAMMER IN TENT PEGS.

One night, a man is hours late home from work. His wife calls his phone again and again, but there's no reply.

She rings her mother in floods of tears. **'I think he must be having an affair, Mum!'** she cries.

Her mother replies: **'Why do you always think the worst? He might have been in a car crash!'**

ALTERNATIVE THINGS TO DO WITH YOUR PHONE #14

USE IT AS AN ICE PICK WHILE SCALING THE MATTERHORN.

THE FIRST EMOJIS WERE CREATED
IN 1999 BY JAPANESE ARTIST
SHIGETAKA KURITA FOR JAPAN'S
MAIN MOBILE CARRIER, DOCOMO.
HE CREATED A SET OF 176 12-BY-
12 PIXEL EMOJIS SHOWING THE
WEATHER, PHASES OF THE MOON,
MODES OF TRANSPORT AND –
OF COURSE – **HEARTS.**

HOW DID EVERYONE KNOW
THAT EVERYONE ELSE
AGREED WITH THEM ABOUT
EVERYTHING BEFORE THEY
INVENTED PHONES?

FIND THE PAIR

Which two phone cases are identical?

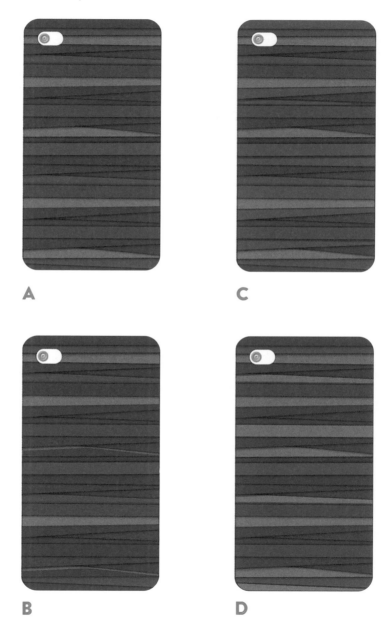

A

C

B

D

E

G

F

H

DO YOUR FAMILY MEMBERS STICK YOUR PHONE TO THEIR FOREHEADS SO THEY CAN PRETEND YOU'RE LOOKING AT THEM WHEN THEY'RE TALKING?

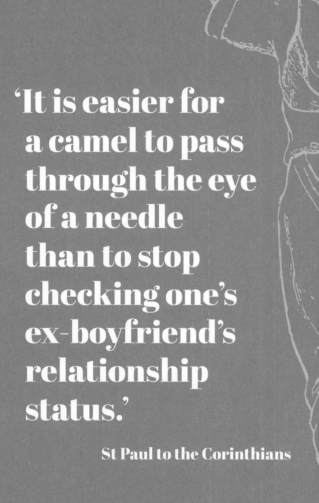

'It is easier for a camel to pass through the eye of a needle than to stop checking one's ex-boyfriend's relationship status.'

St Paul to the Corinthians

ALTERNATIVE THINGS TO DO WITH YOUR PHONE #15

USE IT TO SPREAD THE ICING ON A BATCH OF CHOCOLATE CUPCAKES.

A

B

C

D

E

F

G

H

DATING APP GUESS WHO

John would like to date someone who:

a) does not have a beard

b) does not wear a hat

c) has red hair

Who should he pick?

BLUETOOTH, THE WIRELESS TECHNOLOGY USED FOR EXCHANGING DATA BETWEEN FIXED AND MOBILE DEVICES, IS NAMED AFTER 10TH-CENTURY KING HARALD BLUETOOTH, WHO UNITED DANISH TRIBES INTO ONE KINGDOM.

Because he also liked to listen to the latest Taylor Swift album in the car.

ALTERNATIVE THINGS TO DO WITH YOUR PHONE #16

USE IT AS A BOOKMARK SO YOU DON'T LOSE YOUR PAGE IN *WAR AND PEACE*.

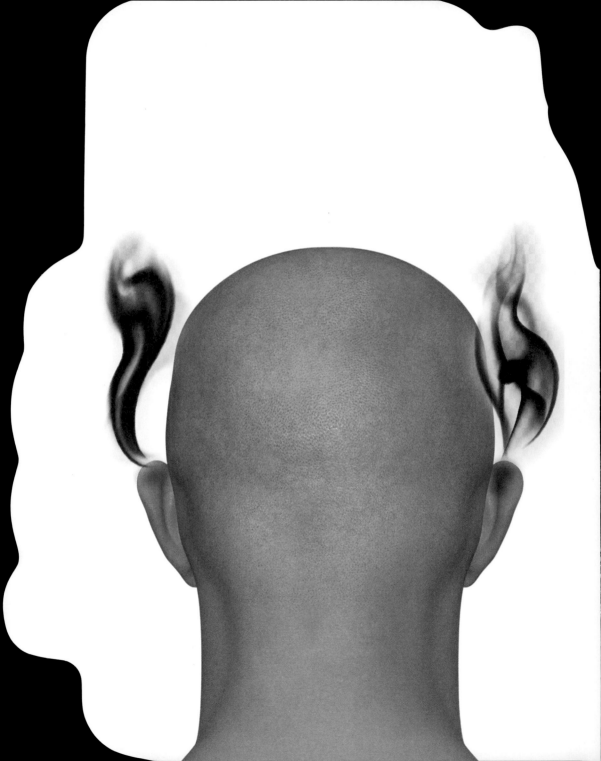

A MAN GOES TO SEE HIS
DOCTOR WITH BURNS ON
BOTH HIS EARS.

'WHAT HAPPENED?' ASKS
THE DOCTOR.

'I WAS DOING THE IRONING
WHEN MY PHONE RANG.
I FORGOT WHAT I WAS
DOING AND PUT THE IRON
TO MY EAR BY ACCIDENT.'

'THAT EXPLAINS ONE EAR.
WHAT ABOUT THE OTHER
ONE?' ASKS THE DOCTOR.

'THE F*@!ER RANG TWICE.'

QUIZ:
DO YOU HAVE FOMO?

1. You check your Instagram feed:

a) hourly

b) every few minutes

c) you don't need to check it because you have the volume on your notifications turned up so the ping will wake you even if you're in a deep sleep

2. You become anxious when all your friends have tagged each other in a photo taken at:

a) a party to which you weren't invited

b) a neighbourhood-watch meeting

c) a landfill

3. You feel jealous when your friend posts photos of herself:

a) in the front row of a Paris fashion show

b) rifling through the bargains in a charity shop

c) cleaning out the dust bunnies at the back of her wardrobe

4. Two friends check in to a bar on Facebook. You:

a) like the status, in the hope it will make them feel bad for not inviting you

b) unfriend them instantly

c) head straight to the bar, then act surprised to bump into them

5. You become convinced that your friend doesn't really like you because he posts that:

a) he has invited his crochet club over for dinner, but not you

b) he has invited his girlfriend over for dinner, but not you

c) he has invited a stray cat in for a bowl of milk, but not you

ALTERNATIVE THINGS TO DO WITH YOUR PHONE #17

ATTACH IT TO STRING AND WRIGGLE IT AROUND FOR YOUR CAT TO POUNCE ON.

A SURVEY BY AN INSURANCE COMPANY REVEALED THAT 50 PER CENT OF PEOPLE USE THEIR PHONE WHILE ON THE TOILET. EVEN MORE DISGUSTINGLY, IT ALSO REVEALED THAT 40 PER CENT HAVE DROPPED THEIR PHONE IN THE SINK... OR DOWN THE TOILET.

SPOT THE DIFFERENCE
CAN YOU SPOT FIVE DIFFERENCES?

TURN OVER FOR THE ANSWER.

DID YOU SPOT THEM?

THE UNICODE CONSORTIUM IS A NON-PROFIT ORGANISATION THAT SELECTS THE EMOJI ICONS USED BY THE WORLD'S SMARTPHONES. THEY BASE THEIR DECISIONS ON SUBMISSIONS FROM INDIVIDUALS AND GROUPS WHO PRESENT A CASE FOR WHY THEIR EMOJI IS ESSENTIAL...

And yet they accepted the Pile of Poo emoji in 2010.

ALTERNATIVE THINGS TO DO WITH YOUR PHONE #18

USE IT AS A PAPERWEIGHT FOR YOUR HAND-WRITTEN HAIKUS.

IT'S SO ANNOYING WHEN SOMEONE TEXTS YOU WHEN YOU'RE IN THE MIDDLE OF TEXTING THEM...
YOU HAVE TO RETYPE THE WHOLE TEXT.

IT'S SO ANNOYING WHEN SOMEONE TEXTS YOU WHEN YOU'RE IN THE MIDDLE OF TEXTING THEM...
YOU HAVE TO RET|

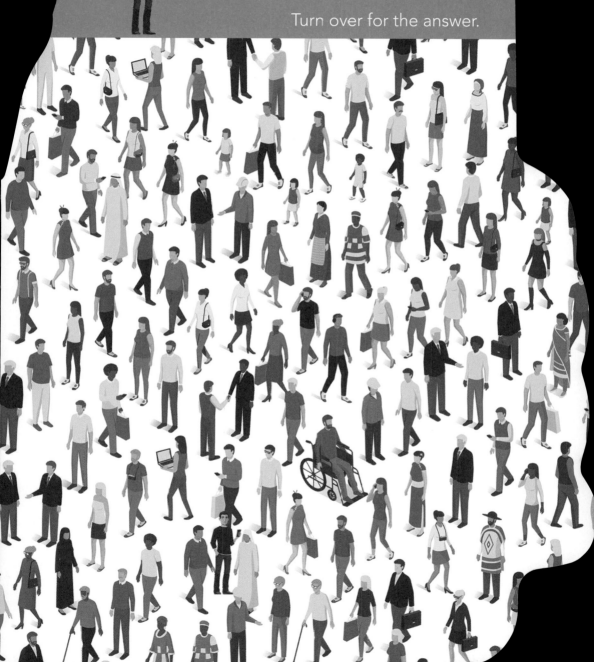

ALTERNATIVE THINGS TO DO WITH YOUR PHONE #19

USE IT AS A PING PONG PADDLE.

'Believe in
your selfie.'

Julius Caesar

HOW DID PEOPLE
CHOOSE LIFE PARTNERS
BASED ON THEIR LOOKS
ALONE BEFORE THEY
INVENTED PHONES?

SPOT THE DIFFERENCE
CAN YOU SPOT FIVE DIFFERENCES?

TURN OVER FOR THE ANSWER.

DID YOU SPOT THEM?

IN 2016, THE PRIDE FLAG
BECAME AN EMOJI, ALONG
WITH A SINGLE DAD AND A
WEIGHTLIFTING WOMAN.

'When mobile phones were first invented, they seemed so convenient. Only when it was too late did we realise they are as convenient as the ball and chain on a convict's bruised ankle.'

Charles Dickens

ALTERNATIVE THINGS TO DO WITH YOUR PHONE #20

USE IT TO SLICE THROUGH TOFU.

FREE YOUR FINGERS FROM
YOUR PHONE.